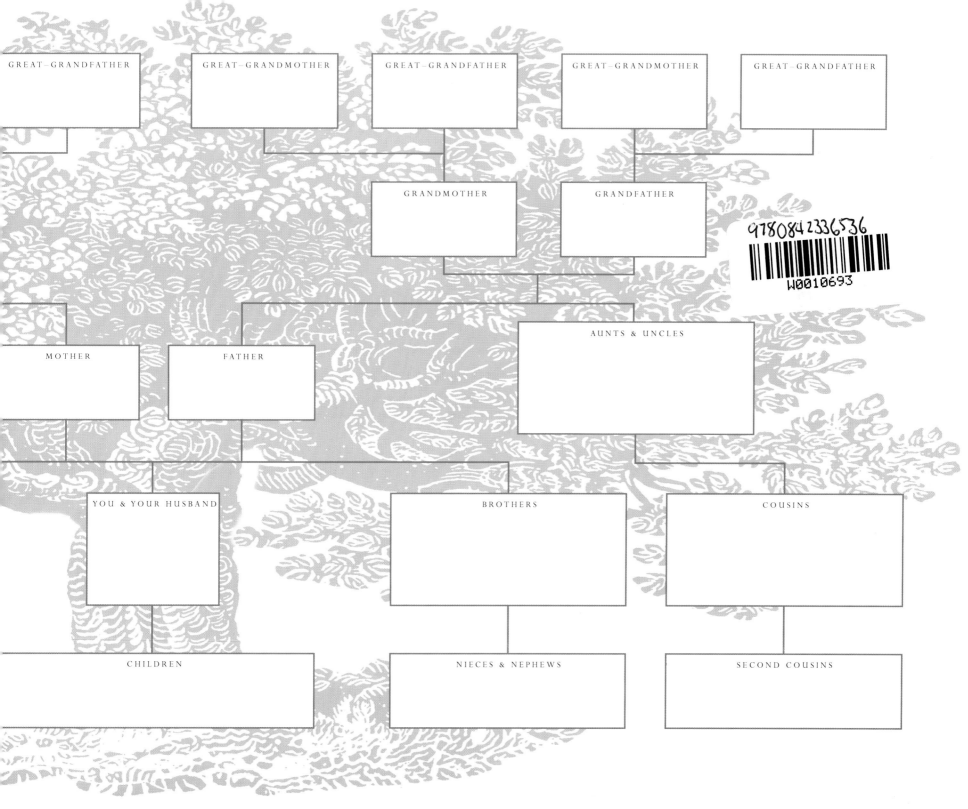

GREAT-GRANDFATHER

GREAT-GRANDMOTHER

GREAT-GRANDFATHER

GREAT-GRANDMOTHER

GREAT-GRANDFATHER

GRANDMOTHER

GRANDFATHER

AUNTS & UNCLES

MOTHER

FATHER

YOU & YOUR HUSBAND

BROTHERS

COUSINS

CHILDREN

NIECES & NEPHEWS

SECOND COUSINS

9780842336536

W0010693

Family – the very word means not only common ancestry and shared physical characteristics, but fellowship, unity, and community. As Roots author, Alex Haley has said, "A family is a link to the past, a bridge to the future." Our family is what helps us understand our past (for better, for worse) and therefore equips us to face current and future challenges.

Families come in all shapes and sizes, but one thing is certain: the Bible tells us that a family is meant to be the place where a mother and father provide wisdom and knowledge, love and nurturing comfort, and moral and spiritual guidance to their children. So it's no wonder that strong, healthy, Christian families are the hope for our fragmented world! Through them we have the marvelous opportunity to pass on biblical values, traditions that emphasize your clan's uniqueness, and stories of moral and spiritual fiber that can help succeeding generations stand strong.

With the fast pace of life, it's even more important to feel a sense of belonging, to learn from ancestors' successes and failures, to anticipate the future with hope and faith, and to build a spiritual legacy. That's why, since the beginning of time, families have kept records of their genealogical roots. They've passed down wit and wisdom, preserved heart-warming memories, and shared spiritual experiences.

That is where *A Christian Family Record Book* comes in – as a tool to help you begin researching your family roots and compiling a personal family tree. You will find space to record interesting facts and cherished anecdotes about members of your and your spouse's families. There is also plenty of room to paste pictures and small mementos.

As you write down relevant facts, intriguing memories, and spiritual highlights, you'll become even more aware of God's working in the lives of those in your genealogy. What a priceless gift for you to pass on to your children and grandchildren!

I have a delightful inheritance.
Psalm 16:6 *NIV*

FOOTPRINTS OF FAITH

A CHRISTIAN FAMILY RECORD BOOK

TYNDALE HOUSE PUBLISHERS, INC.
WHEATON, ILLINOIS

A DK PUBLISHING BOOK

Design Mason Linklater

Managing Art Editor Philip Gilderdale
Managing Editor Jemima Dunne
Senior Art Editor Karen Ward
Production Antony Heller

Special photography David Merewether
Border illustration Jane Thomson

Copyright © 1997
Dorling Kindersley Limited, London

All rights reserved. No part of this publication may be reproduced,
stored in a retrieval system, or transmitted in any form or by any
means, electronic, mechanical, photocopying, recording, or otherwise,
without prior written permission of the copyright owner.

All Scripture quotations, unless otherwise indicated, are taken from
the Holy Bible, New International Version®. NIV®.
Copyright © 1973, 1978, 1984 by International Bible Society.
Used by permission of Zondervan Publishing House. All rights reserved.

Scripture quotations marked NLT are taken from the Holy Bible,
New Living Translation, copyright © 1996. Used by permission of
Tyndale House Publishers, Inc., Wheaton, Illinois 60189. All rights reserved.

This edition published in the United States by
Tyndale House Publishers, Inc.
351 Executive Drive
Carol Stream, Illinois 60188

Visit Tyndale's exciting Web site at www.tyndale.com

ISBN 0-8423-3653-2

Color reproduction by Colorlito Rigogliosi S.R.L., Milan, Italy
Printed and bound by Tien Wah Press, Singapore

04 03 02 01 00 99 98
8 7 6 5 4 3 2 1

ACKNOWLEDGMENTS

DK would like to thank the following for their kind assistance in supplying items for special
photography: Gunvor Avery and Ingrid Mason.

The following photographs were reproduced by courtesy of
London Toy and Model Museum, pages 12, 22, 29; Mattel UK Ltd., page 13;
Faith Eaton Collection, pages 22, 40, 55; Worthing Museum and Art Gallery, page 24;
Judy Sparrow, page 28; Lawleys Ltd., page 37; Paul and Rosemary Volpp, page 46;
National Maritime Museum, page 47.

CONTENTS

You & Your Family

Your Husband's Family

BUILDING YOUR SPIRITUAL HERITAGE

When God created families, he gave us a wonderful gift. After all, who knows you better than your family – and loves you anyway? Through shared history, families provide stability, continuity, and reassurance in this world of rapid change. We celebrate landmark events, applaud each other's triumphs, encourage each other when times are hard, learn from each other, and become better persons as a result. And families with godly values have an even greater bond through prayer, worship, and growing in Christ together. Knowing we're made by a master Creator further sharpens our vision for where we're going on our shared journey of faith.

Every family has it's God-given characteristics – whether of intellect, looks, temperament, or talents – that pass from one generation to the next. And as we look into our past, we see the common threads: maybe your mom has her father's eyes; your daughter has become a teacher like her great-grandparent; or your dad has his grandfather's gift of faith. That's why observing and recording past events and getting to know your heritage can be tremendously rewarding. Here's how to get started.

Setting out on your search

In constructing a family tree, a skillful, seasoned genealogist is able to trace the direct line of descent through many generations, covering hundreds of years with probably thousands of names. Such a search is not only time-consuming but also costly; as an alternative, you can set out on your search with the more modest and achievable aim of compiling the family tree (or "pedigree," as it is known) of your most recent ancestors. Cataloging the accumulated knowledge of your parents should enable you to trace your family tree back as far as your great-grandparents' generation, on both your mother's and your father's side. In the process, you may even turn up long-lost or far-flung relatives who will provide vital clues for research into more distant times.

Sources of information: family stories & papers

First, decide whether to trace your maternal and paternal lines at the same time. Tracing both lines simultaneously will not affect the result, but you may find it less complicated to complete your research into one line before starting on the other. Let family members know you are researching your family tree, and enlist their help to gather as much information as possible, especially details of marriages and children, plus any family stories they would like to contribute.

Sketch out a rough family tree that shows each generation on a separate level and keep a meticulous record of every piece you discover. Update your tree and records as new information emerges, and don't destroy any evidence until you're sure it has no relevance. It's a good idea to visit elderly relatives in person and tape your conversations with them to transcribe and refer to later. Never forget the importance of family Bibles, correspondence, and "forgotten" diaries. So ask around — you may be surprised what turns up.

Matters of public record

Occasionally, you may need to test the accuracy of information received from family members or perhaps some line of enquiry will prove inconclusive. This is the time to consider moving on to a more serious level of research: consulting public records. Start with birth and marriage certificates. Although details vary from one region and time period to another, the basic information is the same. A birth certificate records the individual's name, parents (including the mother's maiden name and the father's occupation), and the date and place of birth. A marriage certificate shows the names of the couple (and their fathers' names), residence and age when married, and the date and place of the ceremony. Wills, census reports, and parochial and civil records also yield useful information. For this level of research, it is worth joining your local genealogical society, which can guide you through the complicated maze of the public record system.

A spiritual legacy for future generations

Dr. James Dobson has said that "A family is literally a museum of memories." Taking time to trace your family tree is an opportunity to gather your own spiritual treasury of remembrance, memento, and fact.

As your quest reveals each new name, write it in your notebook and then go on with your research. Remember, especially if your surname is not unusual, that a name must be verified with biographical detail that clearly identifies that person as a member of your family. Only then can you record the name on the family tree at the front or back of this book.

The detective work involved in tracing your family tree is its own reward, yet small when compared with the satisfaction of discovering the richness of your very own spiritual heritage. Even if your family history may not be all you would like it to be, tracing your ancestry can give you the incentive to create new, healthy, traditions from this point on for yourself and your family.

No matter where you have come from, each day God provides a new beginning to build a strong heritage. As author Maxine Hancock says, "In any given family, there is the potential to change this world for God! " So let the details you uncover bring your family tree to life and transform it into a unique spiritual legacy for future generations.

ALL ABOUT YOU

Significant details

NAME & NICKNAMES

DATE, PLACE & TIME OF BIRTH

DISTINGUISHING FEATURES

TYPICAL FAMILY CHARACTERISTICS

CLOSEST FRIENDS

PHOTOGRAPH

Childhood

CHILDHOOD HOME

EARLIEST MEMORY OF MOTHER & FATHER

MOST & LEAST LIKED FOODS

FAVORITE GAMES & TOYS

BEST FRIENDS

FAMILY PETS

ELEMENTARY SCHOOL

Teenage years

HIGH SCHOOL

FAVORITE SUBJECTS & TEACHERS

SPECIAL FRIENDS

FAVORITE HOBBIES & PASTIMES

FIRST DATE

FAVORITE SINGER OR GROUP & SONG

Adulthood

FURTHER EDUCATION

FIRST JOB

FIRST PAYCHECK

FIRST HOME OR APARTMENT

FAVORITE LEISURE ACTIVITIES OR VACATIONS

LIFE GOALS & ACHIEVEMENTS

MOST SIGNIFICANT SPIRITUAL EVENT

You saw me before I was born.
PSALM 139:16 *NLT*

ALL ABOUT YOUR HUSBAND

Significant details

NAME & NICKNAMES

DATE, PLACE & TIME OF BIRTH

DISTINGUISHING FEATURES

TYPICAL FAMILY CHARACTERISTICS

CLOSEST FRIENDS

PHOTOGRAPH

Childhood

CHILDHOOD HOME

EARLIEST MEMORY OF MOTHER & FATHER

MOST & LEAST LIKED FOODS

FAVORITE GAMES & TOYS

BEST FRIENDS

FAMILY PETS

ELEMENTARY SCHOOL

Teenage years

HIGH SCHOOL

FAVORITE SUBJECTS & TEACHERS

SPECIAL FRIENDS

FAVORITE HOBBIES & PASTIMES

FIRST DATE

FAVORITE SINGER OR GROUP & SONG

Adulthood

FURTHER EDUCATION

FIRST JOB

FIRST PAYCHECK

FIRST HOME OR APARTMENT

FAVORITE LEISURE ACTIVITIES OR VACATIONS

LIFE GOALS & ACHIEVEMENTS

MOST SIGNIFICANT SPIRITUAL EVENT

O LORD, you have searched me and you know me.
PSALM 139:1 *NIV*

*Y*OUR MARRIAGE

HOW YOU & YOUR SPOUSE MET

BRIDESMAIDS, MAID OF HONOR & ATTENDANTS

WHEN & HOW HE PROPOSED

SPECIAL GUESTS

The wedding

DATE, PLACE & TIME OF CEREMONY

RECEPTION SITE

WHAT THE WEATHER WAS LIKE

WEDDING & GOING-AWAY OUTFITS

BEST MAN & USHERS

MEMORABLE MOMENTS OF THE CEREMONY

HONEYMOON MEMORIES

PHOTOGRAPH

PHOTOGRAPH

Your life together

YOUR FIRST HOME

YOUR HOME NOW

YOUR FIRST ANNIVERSARY

HOPES, DREAMS & PRAYERS

HIGHLIGHTS OF YOUR MARRIAGE

Be devoted to one another.
Honor one another above yourselves.
ROMANS 12:10 *NIV*

$\mathscr{Y}$OUR CHILDREN

First child

NAME & NICKNAMES

DATE, PLACE & TIME OF BIRTH

SPECIAL MEMORIES OF THE BIRTH

FIRST WORDS, FIRST STEPS

FIRST BIRTHDAY

FIRST DAY AT SCHOOL

SPECIAL PRAYERS FOR THIS CHILD

Second child

NAME & NICKNAMES

DATE, PLACE & TIME OF BIRTH

SPECIAL MEMORIES OF THE BIRTH

FIRST WORDS, FIRST STEPS

FIRST BIRTHDAY

FIRST DAY AT SCHOOL

SPECIAL PRAYERS FOR THIS CHILD

Sons are a heritage from the LORD,
children a heritage from him.
PSALM 127:3 *NIV*

PHOTOGRAPH

PHOTOGRAPH

PHOTOGRAPH

Third child

NAME & NICKNAMES

FIRST BIRTHDAY

DATE, PLACE & TIME OF BIRTH

FIRST DAY AT SCHOOL

SPECIAL MEMORIES OF THE BIRTH

SPECIAL PRAYERS FOR THIS CHILD

FIRST WORDS, FIRST STEPS

For additional children, copy these pages.

*Y*OUR MOTHER

Significant details

NAME & NICKNAMES

DATE, PLACE & TIME OF BIRTH

DISTINGUISHING FEATURES

TYPICAL FAMILY CHARACTERISTICS

BEST FRIENDS

PHOTOGRAPH

Childhood

CHILDHOOD HOME

SIGNIFICANT MEMORIES OF PARENTS

FAVORITE GAMES & PASTIMES

FAMILY PETS

MOST SIGNIFICANT CHILDHOOD MEMORY

MEMORIES OF SCHOOL & TEACHERS

Adulthood

FURTHER EDUCATION

FIRST JOB, FIRST PAYCHECK

FIRST MEETING WITH YOUR FATHER

FIRST IMPRESSION OF YOUR FATHER

DATE, PLACE & TIME OF MARRIAGE

HONEYMOON MEMORIES

FIRST HOME TOGETHER

FAVORITE HOBBIES & PASTIMES

MOST SIGNIFICANT SPIRITUAL EVENT

LIFE GOALS & ACHIEVEMENTS

Her brothers & sisters

NAME, DATE OF BIRTH

CHILDREN & GRANDCHILDREN

NAME, DATE OF BIRTH

CHILDREN & GRANDCHILDREN

NAME, DATE OF BIRTH

CHILDREN & GRANDCHILDREN

NAME, DATE OF BIRTH

CHILDREN & GRANDCHILDREN

*Her children arise
and call her blessed.*
PROVERBS 31:28 *NIV*

For additional siblings, copy these pages.

Your Father

Significant details

NAME & NICKNAMES

DATE, PLACE & TIME OF BIRTH

DISTINGUISHING FEATURES

TYPICAL FAMILY CHARACTERISTICS

BEST FRIENDS

Childhood

CHILDHOOD HOME

SIGNIFICANT MEMORIES OF PARENTS

FAVORITE GAMES & PASTIMES

FAMILY PETS

MOST SIGNIFICANT CHILDHOOD MEMORY

SPECIAL FRIENDS

MEMORIES OF SCHOOL & TEACHERS

Adulthood

FURTHER EDUCATION

FIRST JOB, FIRST PAYCHECK

WHEN & HOW HE PROPOSED

FIRST IMPRESSION OF YOUR MOTHER

FAVORITE SPORTS & HOBBIES

FAVORITE CITY & VACATION

MEMORABLE EVENTS

MOST SIGNIFICANT SPIRITUAL EVENT

LIFE GOALS & ACHIEVEMENTS

His brothers & sisters

NAME, DATE OF BIRTH

CHILDREN & GRANDCHILDREN

PHOTOGRAPH

NAME, DATE OF BIRTH

CHILDREN & GRANDCHILDREN

NAME, DATE OF BIRTH

CHILDREN & GRANDCHILDREN

NAME, DATE OF BIRTH

CHILDREN & GRANDCHILDREN

NAME, DATE OF BIRTH

CHILDREN & GRANDCHILDREN

The living, the living – they praise you, as I am doing today;
fathers tell their children about your faithfulness.
ISAIAH 38:19 *NIV*

For additional siblings, copy these pages.

Your BROTHERS & SISTERS

Brother

NAME, NICKNAMES & DATE OF BIRTH

TYPICAL FAMILY CHARACTERISTICS

SIGNIFICANT CHILDHOOD MEMORIES

WIFE'S NAME & WEDDING DATE

PAST & PRESENT PLACES LIVED

His children

NAMES, NICKNAMES & DATES OF BIRTH

Grandchildren

NAMES, NICKNAMES & DATES OF BIRTH

PHOTOGRAPH

PHOTOGRAPH

Brother

NAME, NICKNAMES & DATE OF BIRTH

TYPICAL FAMILY CHARACTERISTICS

SIGNIFICANT CHILDHOOD MEMORIES

WIFE'S NAME & WEDDING DATE

PAST & PRESENT PLACES LIVED

His children

NAMES, NICKNAMES & DATES OF BIRTH

Grandchildren

NAMES, NICKNAMES & DATES OF BIRTH

Sister

NAME, NICKNAMES & DATE OF BIRTH

TYPICAL FAMILY CHARACTERISTICS

SIGNIFICANT CHILDHOOD MEMORIES

HUSBAND'S NAME & WEDDING DATE

PAST & PRESENT PLACES LIVED

PHOTOGRAPH

Sister

NAME, NICKNAMES & DATE OF BIRTH

TYPICAL FAMILY CHARACTERISTICS

SIGNIFICANT CHILDHOOD MEMORIES

HUSBAND'S NAME & WEDDING DATE

PAST & PRESENT PLACES LIVED

Her children

NAMES, NICKNAMES & DATES OF BIRTH

Her children

NAMES, NICKNAMES & DATES OF BIRTH

Grandchildren

NAMES, NICKNAMES
& DATES OF BIRTH

PHOTOGRAPH

Grandchildren

NAMES, NICKNAMES & DATES OF BIRTH

*Be encouraged in heart
and united in love.*
COLOSSIANS 2:2 *NIV*

For additional siblings, copy these pages.

$\mathscr{Y}$OUR OTHER CLOSE RELATIVES

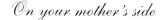

On your mother's side

NAME, NICKNAMES & DATE OF BIRTH

HOW RELATED

CHILDREN & GRANDCHILDREN

SPECIAL FAMILY MEMORIES

PRACTICAL OR SPIRITUAL INSIGHTS

NAME, NICKNAMES & DATE OF BIRTH

HOW RELATED

CHILDREN & GRANDCHILDREN

SPECIAL FAMILY MEMORIES

PRACTICAL OR SPIRITUAL INSIGHTS

PHOTOGRAPH

NAME, NICKNAMES & DATE OF BIRTH

HOW RELATED

CHILDREN & GRANDCHILDREN

SPECIAL FAMILY MEMORIES

PRACTICAL OR SPIRITUAL INSIGHTS

NAME, NICKNAMES & DATE OF BIRTH

HOW RELATED

CHILDREN & GRANDCHILDREN

SPECIAL FAMILY MEMORIES

PRACTICAL OR SPIRITUAL INSIGHTS

On your father's side

NAME, NICKNAMES & DATE OF BIRTH

HOW RELATED

CHILDREN & GRANDCHILDREN

SPECIAL FAMILY MEMORIES

PRACTICAL OR SPIRITUAL INSIGHTS

NAME, NICKNAMES
& DATE OF BIRTH

HOW RELATED

CHILDREN & GRANDCHILDREN

SPECIAL FAMILY MEMORIES

PRACTICAL OR SPIRITUAL INSIGHTS

PHOTOGRAPH

NAME, NICKNAMES & DATE OF BIRTH

HOW RELATED

CHILDREN & GRANDCHILDREN

SPECIAL FAMILY MEMORIES

PRACTICAL OR SPIRITUAL INSIGHTS

NAME, NICKNAMES & DATE OF BIRTH

HOW RELATED

CHILDREN & GRANDCHILDREN

SPECIAL FAMILY MEMORIES

PRACTICAL OR SPIRITUAL INSIGHTS

Every time I think of you,
I give thanks to my God.
PHILIPPIANS 1:3 *NLT*

Your MATERNAL GRANDMOTHER

Significant details

NAME & NICKNAMES

DATE & PLACE OF BIRTH

DISTINGUISHING FEATURES

Typical Family Characteristics

Childhood

CHILDHOOD HOME

FAVORITE ACTIVITIES

MEMORIES OF PARENTS

MEMORIES OF SCHOOL

PHOTOGRAPH

Adulthood

FURTHER EDUCATION

FIRST JOB, FIRST PAYCHECK

FIRST MEETING WITH YOUR GRANDFATHER

FIRST IMPRESSION OF YOUR GRANDFATHER

FIRST HOME

MEMORABLE MOMENTS & ACHIEVEMENTS

FAVORITE SAYING OR INSIGHT

MOST SIGNIFICANT SPIRITUAL EVENT

Her brothers & sisters

NAME, DATE OF BIRTH

CHILDREN & GRANDCHILDREN

NAME, DATE OF BIRTH

CHILDREN & GRANDCHILDREN

NAME, DATE OF BIRTH

CHILDREN & GRANDCHILDREN

NAME, DATE OF BIRTH

CHILDREN & GRANDCHILDREN

NAME, DATE OF BIRTH

CHILDREN & GRANDCHILDREN

*Lord, you have been our dwelling place
throughout all generations.*
PSALM 90:1 *NIV*

For additional siblings, copy these pages.

*Y*OUR MATERNAL GRANDFATHER

Significant details

NAME & NICKNAMES

DATE & PLACE OF BIRTH

DISTINGUISHING FEATURES

TYPICAL FAMILY CHARACTERISTICS

PHOTOGRAPH

Childhood

CHILDHOOD HOME

FAVORITE ACTIVITIES

MEMORIES OF PARENTS

MEMORIES OF SCHOOL

Adulthood

FURTHER EDUCATION

FIRST JOB

FIRST PAYCHECK

WHEN & HOW HE PROPOSED

FIRST IMPRESSION OF YOUR GRANDMOTHER

HONEYMOON MEMORIES

GRANDPARENTS' HOME YOU REMEMBER

FAVORITE HOBBIES & PASTIMES

MEMORABLE JOURNEYS & EVENTS

His brothers & sisters

NAME

DATE OF BIRTH

CHILDREN

NAME

DATE OF BIRTH

CHILDREN

NAME

DATE OF BIRTH

CHILDREN

NAME

DATE OF BIRTH

CHILDREN

NAMES OF OTHER SIBLINGS

The righteous man leads a blameless life;
blessed are his children after him.
PROVERBS 20:7 *NIV*

Your PATERNAL GRANDMOTHER

Significant details

NAME & NICKNAMES

DATE & PLACE OF BIRTH

DISTINGUISHING FEATURES

TYPICAL FAMILY CHARACTERISTICS

Childhood

CHILDHOOD HOME

FAVORITE ACTIVITIES

MEMORIES OF PARENTS

MEMORIES OF SCHOOL

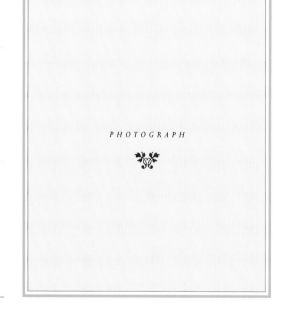

PHOTOGRAPH

Adulthood

FURTHER EDUCATION

FIRST JOB, FIRST PAYCHECK

FIRST MEETING WITH YOUR GRANDFATHER

FIRST IMPRESSION OF YOUR GRANDFATHER

FIRST HOME

MEMORABLE MOMENTS & ACHIEVEMENTS

FAVORITE SAYING OR INSIGHT

MOST SIGNIFICANT SPIRITUAL EVENT

Gray hair is a crown of glory;
it is gained by living a godly life.
PROVERBS 16:31 *NLT*

Her brothers & sisters

NAME, DATE OF BIRTH

CHILDREN & GRANDCHILDREN

NAME, DATE OF BIRTH

CHILDREN & GRANDCHILDREN

NAME, DATE OF BIRTH

CHILDREN & GRANDCHILDREN

NAME, DATE OF BIRTH

CHILDREN & GRANDCHILDREN

NAME, DATE OF BIRTH

CHILDREN & GRANDCHILDREN

NAME, DATE OF BIRTH

CHILDREN & GRANDCHILDREN

For additional siblings, copy these pages.

*Y*OUR PATERNAL GRANDFATHER

Significant details

NAME & NICKNAMES

DATE & PLACE OF BIRTH

DISTINGUISHING FEATURES

TYPICAL FAMILY CHARACTERISTICS

Childhood

CHILDHOOD HOME

FAVORITE ACTIVITIES

MEMORIES OF PARENTS

MEMORIES OF SCHOOL

Adulthood

FURTHER EDUCATION

FIRST JOB, FIRST PAYCHECK

WHEN & HOW HE PROPOSED

FIRST IMPRESSION OF YOUR GRANDMOTHER

GRANDPARENTS' HOME YOU REMEMBER

PHOTOGRAPH

MEMORABLE MOMENTS & ACHIEVEMENTS

FAVORITE SAYING OR INSIGHT

MOST SIGNIFICANT
SPIRITUAL EVENT

His brothers & sisters

NAME, DATE OF BIRTH

CHILDREN & GRANDCHILDREN

NAME, DATE OF BIRTH

CHILDREN & GRANDCHILDREN

NAME, DATE OF BIRTH

CHILDREN & GRANDCHILDREN

NAME, DATE OF BIRTH

CHILDREN & GRANDCHILDREN

NAME, DATE OF BIRTH

CHILDREN & GRANDCHILDREN

NAME, DATE OF BIRTH

CHILDREN & GRANDCHILDREN

He who fears the LORD has a secure fortress,
and for his children it will be a refuge.
PROVERBS 14:26 *NIV*

For additional siblings, copy these pages.

*Y*OUR GREAT-GRANDPARENTS

Maternal grandmother's mother

NAME

....

DATE & PLACE OF BIRTH

....

WHEN & WHERE MARRIED

....

MOST SIGNIFICANT SPIRITUAL EVENT

PHOTOGRAPH

Maternal grandfather's mother

NAME

....

DATE & PLACE OF BIRTH

....

WHEN & WHERE MARRIED

....

MOST SIGNIFICANT SPIRITUAL EVENT

PHOTOGRAPH

Maternal grandmother's father

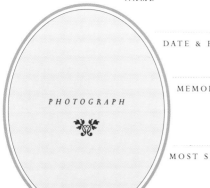

PHOTOGRAPH

NAME

....

DATE & PLACE OF BIRTH

....

MEMORABLE MOMENTS & ACHIEVEMENTS

....

MOST SIGNIFICANT SPIRITUAL EVENT

Maternal grandfather's father

PHOTOGRAPH

NAME

....

DATE & PLACE OF BIRTH

....

MEMORABLE MOMENTS & ACHIEVEMENTS

....

MOST SIGNIFICANT
SPIRITUAL EVENT

Paternal grandmother's mother

NAME

DATE & PLACE OF BIRTH

WHEN & WHERE MARRIED

PHOTOGRAPH

MOST SIGNIFICANT SPIRITUAL EVENT

Paternal grandfather's mother

NAME

DATE & PLACE OF BIRTH

WHEN & WHERE MARRIED

PHOTOGRAPH

MOST SIGNIFICANT SPIRITUAL EVENT

Paternal grandmother's father

NAME

PHOTOGRAPH

DATE & PLACE OF BIRTH

MEMORABLE MOMENTS & ACHIEVEMENTS

MOST SIGNIFICANT SPIRITUAL EVENT

Paternal grandfather's father

NAME

PHOTOGRAPH

DATE & PLACE OF BIRTH

MEMORABLE MOMENTS & ACHIEVEMENTS

MOST SIGNIFICANT SPIRITUAL EVENT

Blessed are the people whose God is the LORD.
PSALM 144:15 *NIV*

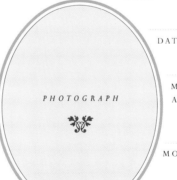

*Y*OUR SPIRITUAL HERITAGE

Spiritual leaders on your mother's side

NAME

HOW RELATED TO YOU

WHEN & HOW BECAME A CHRISTIAN

SPIRITUAL IMPACT ON THE FAMILY

NAME

HOW RELATED TO YOU

WHEN & HOW BECAME A CHRISTIAN

SPIRITUAL IMPACT ON THE FAMILY

NAME

HOW RELATED TO YOU

WHEN & HOW BECAME A CHRISTIAN

SPIRITUAL IMPACT ON THE FAMILY

NAME

HOW RELATED TO YOU

WHEN & HOW BECAME A CHRISTIAN

SPIRITUAL IMPACT ON THE FAMILY

PHOTOGRAPH

Spiritual leaders on your father's side

NAME

HOW RELATED TO YOU

WHEN & HOW BECAME A CHRISTIAN

SPIRITUAL IMPACT ON THE FAMILY

PHOTOGRAPH

NAME

HOW RELATED TO YOU

WHEN & HOW BECAME A CHRISTIAN

SPIRITUAL IMPACT ON THE FAMILY

NAME

HOW RELATED TO YOU

WHEN & HOW BECAME A CHRISTIAN

SPIRITUAL IMPACT ON THE FAMILY

NAME

HOW RELATED TO YOU

WHEN & HOW BECAME A CHRISTIAN

SPIRITUAL IMPACT ON THE FAMILY

They will proclaim his righteousness to a people yet unborn
PSALM 22:3 *NIV*

FAMILY STORIES & ANECDOTES

STORIES ABOUT YOU

FUNNY ANECDOTES FROM EVERYDAY LIFE

STORIES ABOUT YOUR BROTHERS & SISTERS

MEMORABLE HOLIDAY MOMENTS

PHOTOGRAPH

VACATION OR PET STORIES

I will utter things from of old –
what we have heard and known,
what our fathers have told us.
PSALM 78:2-3 *NIV*

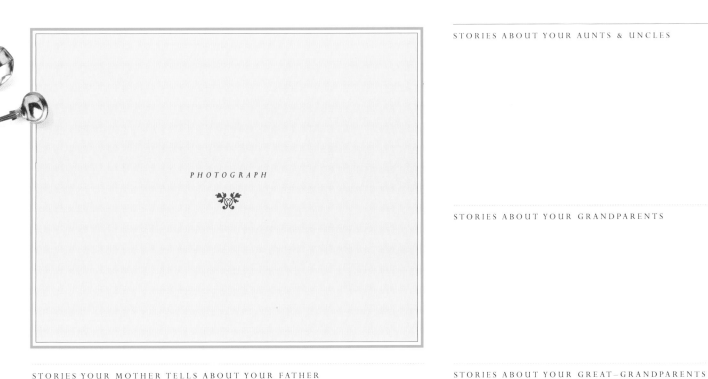

PHOTOGRAPH

STORIES ABOUT YOUR AUNTS & UNCLES

STORIES ABOUT YOUR GRANDPARENTS

STORIES YOUR MOTHER TELLS ABOUT YOUR FATHER

STORIES ABOUT YOUR GREAT-GRANDPARENTS

STORIES YOUR FATHER TELLS ABOUT YOUR MOTHER

SPIRITUAL REMEMBRANCES

Your HUSBAND'S MOTHER

Significant details

NAME & NICKNAMES

DATE, PLACE & TIME OF BIRTH

DISTINGUISHING FEATURES

TYPICAL FAMILY CHARACTERISTICS

BEST FRIENDS

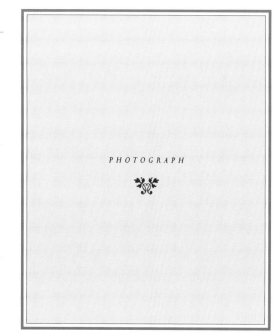

PHOTOGRAPH

Childhood

CHILDHOOD HOME

SIGNIFICANT MEMORIES OF PARENTS

FAVORITE GAMES & PASTIMES

FAMILY PETS

MOST SIGNIFICANT CHILDHOOD MEMORY

SPECIAL FRIENDS

MEMORIES OF SCHOOL & TEACHERS

Adulthood

FURTHER EDUCATION

FIRST JOB, FIRST PAYCHECK

FIRST MEETING WITH HIS FATHER

FIRST IMPRESSION OF HIS FATHER

DATE, PLACE & TIME OF MARRIAGE

FIRST HOME TOGETHER

FAVORITE HOBBIES & PASTIMES

MOST SIGNIFICANT SPIRITUAL EVENT

LIFE GOALS & ACHIEVEMENTS

Her brothers & sisters

NAME, DATE OF BIRTH

CHILDREN & GRANDCHILDREN

NAME, DATE OF BIRTH

CHILDREN & GRANDCHILDREN

NAME, DATE OF BIRTH

CHILDREN & GRANDCHILDREN

NAME, DATE OF BIRTH

CHILDREN & GRANDCHILDREN

NAME, DATE OF BIRTH

CHILDREN & GRANDCHILDREN

As for me and my family,
we will serve the LORD.
JOSHUA 24:15 *NLT*

For additional siblings, copy these pages.

*Y*OUR HUSBAND'S FATHER

Significant details

NAME & NICKNAMES

DATE, PLACE & TIME OF BIRTH

DISTINGUISHING FEATURES

TYPICAL FAMILY CHARACTERISTICS

BEST FRIENDS

PHOTOGRAPH

Childhood

CHILDHOOD HOME

SIGNIFICANT MEMORIES OF PARENTS

FAVORITE GAMES & PASTIMES

FAMILY PETS

MOST SIGNIFICANT CHILDHOOD MEMORY

SPECIAL FRIENDS

MEMORIES OF SCHOOL & TEACHERS

*I guide you in the way of wisdom
and lead you along straight paths.*
PROVERBS 4:11 *NIV*

Adulthood

FURTHER EDUCATION

FIRST JOB, FIRST PAYCHECK

WHEN & HOW HE PROPOSED

FIRST IMPRESSION

FAVORITE SPORTS & HOBBIES

FAVORITE CITY & VACATION

MEMORABLE EVENTS

MOST SIGNIFICANT SPIRITUAL EVENT

LIFE GOALS & ACHIEVEMENTS

His brothers & sisters

NAME, DATE OF BIRTH

CHILDREN & GRANDCHILDREN

NAME, DATE OF BIRTH

CHILDREN & GRANDCHILDREN

NAME, DATE OF BIRTH

CHILDREN & GRANDCHILDREN

NAME, DATE OF BIRTH

CHILDREN & GRANDCHILDREN

NAME, DATE OF BIRTH

CHILDREN & GRANDCHILDREN

For additional siblings, copy these pages.

*Y*OUR HUSBAND'S BROTHERS & SISTERS

Brother

NAME, NICKNAMES & DATE OF BIRTH

TYPICAL FAMILY CHARACTERISTICS

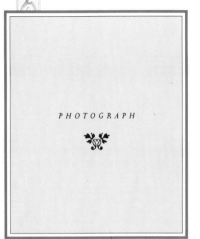

PHOTOGRAPH

SIGNIFICANT CHILDHOOD MEMORIES

WIFE'S NAME & WEDDING DATE

PAST & PRESENT PLACES LIVED

His children

NAMES, NICKNAMES & DATES OF BIRTH

Grandchildren

NAMES, NICKNAMES & DATES OF BIRTH

Brother

NAME, NICKNAMES & DATE OF BIRTH

TYPICAL FAMILY CHARACTERISTICS

PHOTOGRAPH

SIGNIFICANT CHILDHOOD MEMORIES

WIFE'S NAME & WEDDING DATE

PAST & PRESENT PLACES LIVED

His children

NAMES, NICKNAMES & DATES OF BIRTH

Grandchildren

NAMES, NICKNAMES & DATES OF BIRTH

Sister

NAME, NICKNAMES & DATE OF BIRTH

TYPICAL FAMILY CHARACTERISTICS

SIGNIFICANT CHILDHOOD MEMORIES

PHOTOGRAPH

HUSBAND'S NAME & WEDDING DATE

PAST & PRESENT PLACES LIVED

Sister

NAME, NICKNAMES & DATE OF BIRTH

TYPICAL FAMILY CHARACTERISTICS

SIGNIFICANT CHILDHOOD MEMORIES

PHOTOGRAPH

HUSBAND'S NAME & WEDDING DATE

PAST & PRESENT PLACES LIVED

Her children

NAMES, NICKNAMES & DATES OF BIRTH

Her children

NAMES, NICKNAMES & DATES OF BIRTH

Grandchildren

NAMES, NICKNAMES & DATES OF BIRTH

Grandchildren

NAMES, NICKNAMES & DATES OF BIRTH

How good and pleasant it is when brothers live together in unity!
PSALM 133:1 *NIV*

For additional siblings, copy these pages.

Your Husband's Other Close Relatives

On his mother's side

NAME, NICKNAMES & DATE OF BIRTH

HOW RELATED

CHILDREN & GRANDCHILDREN

SPECIAL FAMILY MEMORIES

PRACTICAL OR SPIRITUAL INSIGHTS

PHOTOGRAPH

NAME, NICKNAMES & DATE OF BIRTH

HOW RELATED

CHILDREN & GRANDCHILDREN

SPECIAL FAMILY MEMORIES

PRACTICAL OR SPIRITUAL INSIGHTS

NAME, NICKNAMES & DATE OF BIRTH

HOW RELATED

CHILDREN & GRANDCHILDREN

SPECIAL FAMILY MEMORIES

PRACTICAL OR SPIRITUAL INSIGHTS

PHOTOGRAPH

NAME, NICKNAMES & DATE OF BIRTH

HOW RELATED

CHILDREN & GRANDCHILDREN

SPECIAL FAMILY MEMORIES

PRACTICAL OR SPIRITUAL INSIGHTS

On his father's side

NAME, NICKNAMES & DATE OF BIRTH

HOW RELATED

CHILDREN & GRANDCHILDREN

SPECIAL FAMILY MEMORIES

PRACTICAL OR SPIRITUAL INSIGHTS

NAME, NICKNAMES & DATE OF BIRTH

HOW RELATED

CHILDREN & GRANDCHILDREN

SPECIAL FAMILY MEMORIES

PRACTICAL OR SPIRITUAL INSIGHTS

Love always protects, always trusts,
always hopes, always perseveres.
1 CORINTHIANS 13:7 *NIV*

PHOTOGRAPH

NAME, NICKNAMES & DATE OF BIRTH

HOW RELATED

CHILDREN & GRANDCHILDREN

SPECIAL FAMILY MEMORIES

PRACTICAL OR SPIRITUAL INSIGHTS

NAME, NICKNAMES & DATE OF BIRTH

HOW RELATED

CHILDREN & GRANDCHILDREN

SPECIAL FAMILY MEMORIES

PRACTICAL OR SPIRITUAL INSIGHTS

YOUR HUSBAND'S MATERNAL GRANDMOTHER

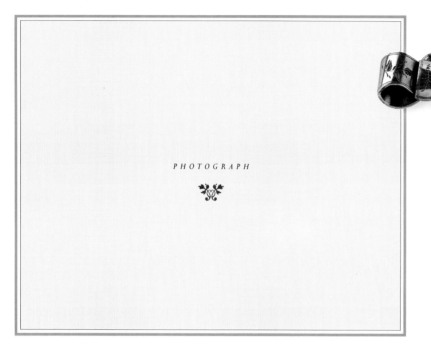

PHOTOGRAPH

TYPICAL FAMILY CHARACTERISTICS

Childhood

CHILDHOOD HOME

FAVORITE ACTIVITIES

MEMORIES OF PARENTS

MEMORIES OF SCHOOL

Significant details

NAME & NICKNAMES

DATE & PLACE OF BIRTH

DISTINGUISHING FEATURES

Let this be written for a future generation,
that a people not yet created may praise the LORD.
PSALM 102:18 NIV

Adulthood

FURTHER EDUCATION

FIRST JOB, FIRST PAYCHECK

FIRST MEETING WITH HIS GRANDFATHER

FIRST IMPRESSION OF HIS GRANDFATHER

FIRST HOME

MEMORABLE MOMENTS & ACHIEVEMENTS

FAVORITE SAYING OR INSIGHT

MOST SIGNIFICANT SPIRITUAL EVENT

Her brothers & sisters

NAME, DATE OF BIRTH

CHILDREN & GRANDCHILDREN

NAME, DATE OF BIRTH

CHILDREN & GRANDCHILDREN

NAME, DATE OF BIRTH

CHILDREN & GRANDCHILDREN

NAME, DATE OF BIRTH

CHILDREN & GRANDCHILDREN

NAME, DATE OF BIRTH

CHILDREN & GRANDCHILDREN

For additional siblings, copy these pages.

$\mathscr{Y}$OUR HUSBAND'S MATERNAL GRANDFATHER

Significant details

NAME & NICKNAMES

DATE & PLACE OF BIRTH

DISTINGUISHING FEATURES

TYPICAL FAMILY CHARACTERISTICS

PHOTOGRAPH

Childhood

CHILDHOOD HOME

FAVORITE ACTIVITIES

MEMORIES OF PARENTS

MEMORIES OF SCHOOL

*A good man leaves an inheritance
for his children's children.*
PROVERBS 13:22 *NIV*

Adulthood

FURTHER EDUCATION

FIRST JOB, FIRST PAYCHECK

WHEN & HOW HE PROPOSED

FIRST IMPRESSION

GRANDPARENTS' HOME YOUR HUSBAND REMEMBERS

FAVORITE HOBBIES & PASTIMES

MEMORABLE MOMENTS & ACHIEVEMENTS

FAVORITE SAYING OR INSIGHT

MOST SIGNIFICANT SPIRITUAL EVENT

His brothers & sisters

NAME, DATE OF BIRTH

CHILDREN & GRANDCHILDREN

NAME, DATE OF BIRTH

CHILDREN & GRANDCHILDREN

NAME, DATE OF BIRTH

CHILDREN & GRANDCHILDREN

NAME, DATE OF BIRTH

CHILDREN & GRANDCHILDREN

NAME, DATE OF BIRTH

CHILDREN & GRANDCHILDREN

For additional siblings, copy these pages.

*Y*OUR HUSBAND'S PATERNAL GRANDMOTHER

Significant details

NAME & NICKNAMES

DATE & PLACE OF BIRTH

DISTINGUISHING FEATURES

FAMILY CHARACTERISTICS

PHOTOGRAPH

Childhood

CHILDHOOD HOME

FAVORITE ACTIVITIES

MEMORIES OF PARENTS

MEMORIES OF SCHOOL

*The path of the righteous
is like the first gleam of dawn,
shining ever brighter.*
PROVERBS 4:18 *NIV*

Adulthood

FURTHER EDUCATION

FIRST JOB, FIRST PAYCHECK

FIRST MEETING WITH HIS GRANDFATHER

FIRST IMPRESSION OF HIS GRANDFATHER

FIRST HOME

MEMORABLE MOMENTS & ACHIEVEMENTS

FAVORITE SAYING OR INSIGHT

MOST SIGNIFICANT SPIRITUAL EVENT

Her brothers & sisters

NAME, DATE OF BIRTH

CHILDREN & GRANDCHILDREN

NAME, DATE OF BIRTH

CHILDREN & GRANDCHILDREN

NAME, DATE OF BIRTH

CHILDREN & GRANDCHILDREN

NAME, DATE OF BIRTH

CHILDREN & GRANDCHILDREN

NAME, DATE OF BIRTH

CHILDREN & GRANDCHILDREN

For additional siblings, copy these pages.

Your HUSBAND'S PATERNAL GRANDFATHER

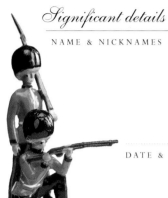

Significant details

NAME & NICKNAMES

DATE & PLACE OF BIRTH

DISTINGUISHING FEATURES

TYPICAL FAMILY CHARACTERISTICS

Posterity will serve him;
future generations
will be told about the Lord.
PSALM 22:30 *NIV*

Childhood

CHILDHOOD HOME

FAVORITE ACTIVITIES

MEMORIES OF PARENTS

PHOTOGRAPH

MEMORIES OF SCHOOL

Adulthood

FURTHER EDUCATION

FIRST JOB, FIRST PAYCHECK

WHEN & HOW HE PROPOSED

FIRST IMPRESSION

GRANDPARENTS' HOME YOUR HUSBAND REMEMBERS

MEMORABLE MOMENTS & ACHIEVEMENTS

FAVORITE SAYING OR INSIGHT

MOST SIGNIFICANT SPIRITUAL EVENT

His brothers & sisters

NAME, DATE OF BIRTH

CHILDREN & GRANDCHILDREN

NAME, DATE OF BIRTH

CHILDREN & GRANDCHILDREN

NAME, DATE OF BIRTH

CHILDREN & GRANDCHILDREN

NAME, DATE OF BIRTH

CHILDREN & GRANDCHILDREN

NAME, DATE OF BIRTH

CHILDREN & GRANDCHILDREN

For additional siblings, copy these pages.

Your Husband's Great-Grandparents

Maternal grandmother's mother

NAME

DATE & PLACE OF BIRTH

WHEN & WHERE MARRIED

PHOTOGRAPH

MOST SIGNIFICANT SPIRITUAL EVENT

Maternal grandfather's mother

NAME

DATE & PLACE OF BIRTH

WHEN & WHERE MARRIED

PHOTOGRAPH

MOST SIGNIFICANT SPIRITUAL EVENT

Maternal grandmother's father

NAME

PHOTOGRAPH

DATE & PLACE OF BIRTH

MEMORABLE MOMENTS & ACHIEVEMENTS

MOST SIGNIFICANT SPIRITUAL EVENT

Maternal grandfather's father

NAME

PHOTOGRAPH

DATE & PLACE OF BIRTH

MEMORABLE MOMENTS & ACHIEVEMENTS

MOST SIGNIFICANT SPIRITUAL EVENT

Paternal grandmother's mother

NAME

DATE & PLACE OF BIRTH

WHEN & WHERE MARRIED

PHOTOGRAPH

MOST SIGNIFICANT SPIRITUAL EVENT

Paternal grandfather's mother

NAME

DATE & PLACE OF BIRTH

WHEN & WHERE MARRIED

PHOTOGRAPH

MOST SIGNIFICANT SPIRITUAL EVENT

Paternal grandmother's father

NAME

PHOTOGRAPH

DATE & PLACE OF BIRTH

MEMORABLE MOMENTS & ACHIEVEMENTS

MOST SIGNIFICANT SPIRITUAL EVENT

Paternal grandfather's father

NAME

PHOTOGRAPH

DATE & PLACE OF BIRTH

MEMORABLE MOMENTS & ACHIEVEMENTS

MOST SIGNIFICANT
SPIRITUAL EVENT

The generation of the upright will be blessed.
PSALM 112:2 *NIV*

Your Husband's Spiritual Heritage

Spiritual leaders on his mother's side

NAME

HOW RELATED TO YOU

WHEN & HOW BECAME A CHRISTIAN

SPIRITUAL IMPACT ON THE FAMILY

NAME

HOW RELATED TO YOU

WHEN & HOW BECAME A CHRISTIAN

SPIRITUAL IMPACT ON THE FAMILY

PHOTOGRAPH

NAME

HOW RELATED TO YOU

WHEN & HOW BECAME A CHRISTIAN

SPIRITUAL IMPACT ON THE FAMILY

NAME

HOW RELATED TO YOU

WHEN & HOW BECAME A CHRISTIAN

SPIRITUAL IMPACT ON THE FAMILY

One generation will commend your works to another;
they will tell of your mighty acts.
PSALM 145:4 *NIV*

Spiritual leaders on his father's side

NAME

HOW RELATED TO YOU

WHEN & HOW BECAME A CHRISTIAN

SPIRITUAL IMPACT ON THE FAMILY

PHOTOGRAPH

NAME

HOW RELATED TO YOU

WHEN & HOW BECAME A CHRISTIAN

SPIRITUAL IMPACT ON THE FAMILY

NAME

HOW RELATED TO YOU

WHEN & HOW BECAME A CHRISTIAN

SPIRITUAL IMPACT ON THE FAMILY

PHOTOGRAPH

NAME

HOW RELATED TO YOU

WHEN & HOW BECAME A CHRISTIAN

SPIRITUAL IMPACT ON THE FAMILY

FAMILY STORIES & ANECDOTES

STORIES ABOUT HIM

MEMORABLE HOLIDAY MOMENTS

STORIES ABOUT HIS BROTHERS & SISTERS

VACATION OR PET STORIES

FUNNY ANECDOTES FROM EVERYDAY LIFE

PHOTOGRAPH

STORIES HIS MOTHER TELLS ABOUT HIS FATHER

STORIES ABOUT HIS GRANDPARENTS

PHOTOGRAPH

PHOTOGRAPH

STORIES HIS FATHER TELLS ABOUT HIS MOTHER

STORIES ABOUT HIS GREAT–GRANDPARENTS

STORIES ABOUT HIS AUNTS & UNCLES

SPIRITUAL REMEMBRANCES

We will tell the next generation the praiseworthy deeds of the LORD.
PSALM 78:4 *NIV*

FAMILY TREE

As a beautiful reminder of your husband's family's history —
and the way God has grown his clan through the generations —
write the name of each member in the intertwining tree branches.
This will create a lasting, visual legacy to pass on to your children.

FAMILY PHOTOGRAPH

GREAT–GRANDMOTHER

GREAT–GRANDFATHER

GREAT–GRANDMOTHER

GRANDMOTHER

GRANDFATHER

AUNTS & UNCLES

COUSINS

SISTERS

SECOND COUSINS

NIECES & NEPHEWS